Little Funnies is a delightful collection of picture books made to put a giggle into storytime.

There are funny stories about a laughing lobster, a daring mouse, a teeny tiny woman, and lots more colourful characters!

Perfect for sharing, these rib-tickling tales will have your little ones coming back for more!

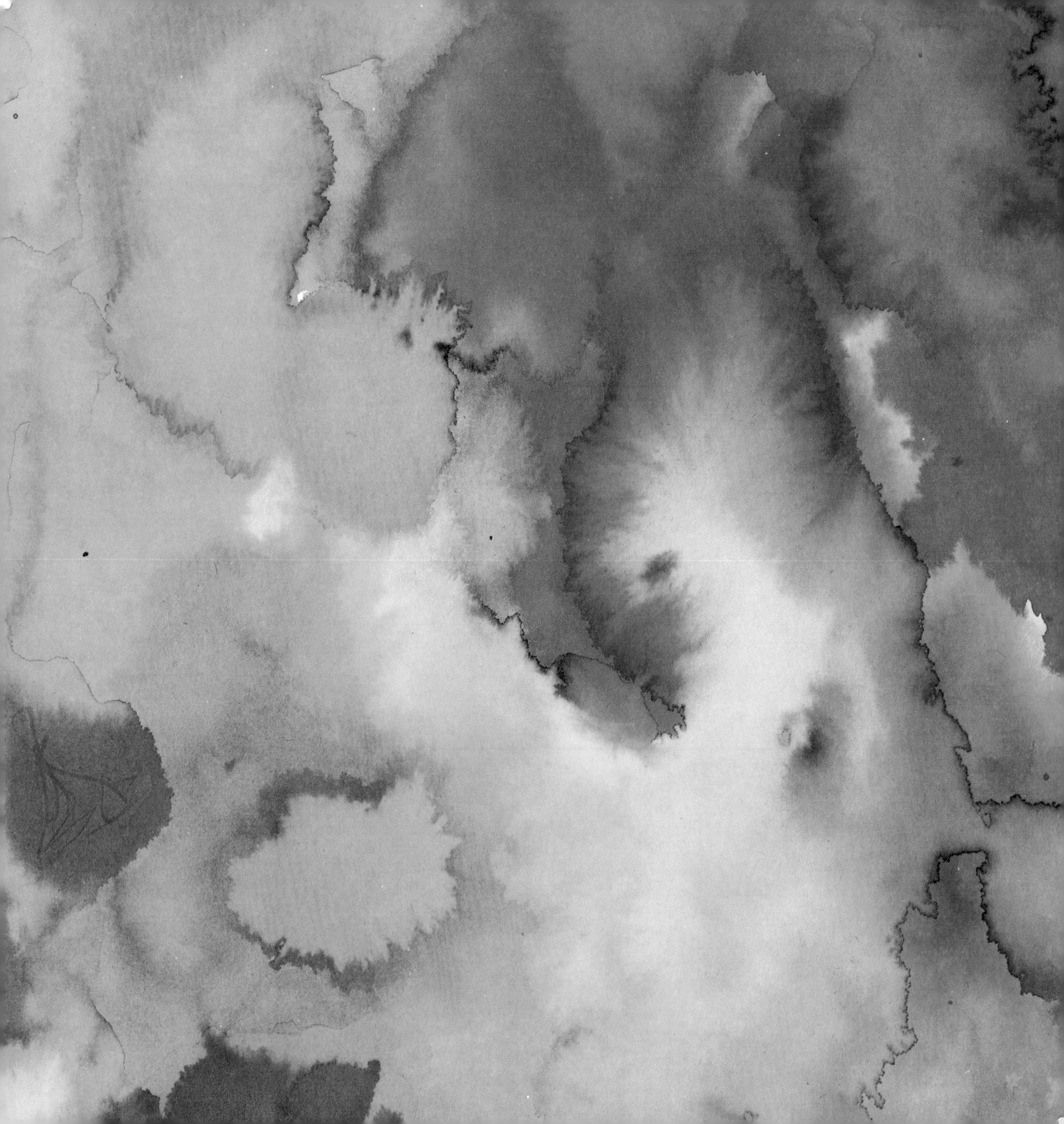

For Deirdre

First published 1995 by Walker Books Ltd
87 Vauxhall Walk, London SE11 5HJ

This edition published 2007

10 9 8 7 6 5 4 3 2 1

This book has been typeset in Plantin.

Printed in China

British Library Cataloguing in Publication Data:
a catalogue record for this book is
available from the British Library.

ISBN 978-1-4063-0794-8

www.walkerbooks.co.uk

"ONLY JOKING!" LAUGHED THE LOBSTER

Colin West

WALKER BOOKS
AND SUBSIDIARIES
LONDON • BOSTON • SYDNEY • AUCKLAND

Look out, Fish, there's a shark following you!

“Only joking!” laughed the lobster.

Look out, Eel, there's a great big shark following you!

"Only joking!" laughed the lobster.

Look out, Crab, there's a great big ugly shark following you!

"Only joking!" laughed the lobster.

Look out, Turtle, there's a great big ugly wild-looking shark following you!

“Only joking!” laughed the lobster.

Look out, Octopus, there's a great big ugly wild-looking mean old shark following you!

"Only joking!" laughed the lobster.

Look out, Shark,
there's a great big ugly
wild-looking mean old
hungry shark …

"SWALLOWING YOU!"
said the shark.

And he wasn't joking!

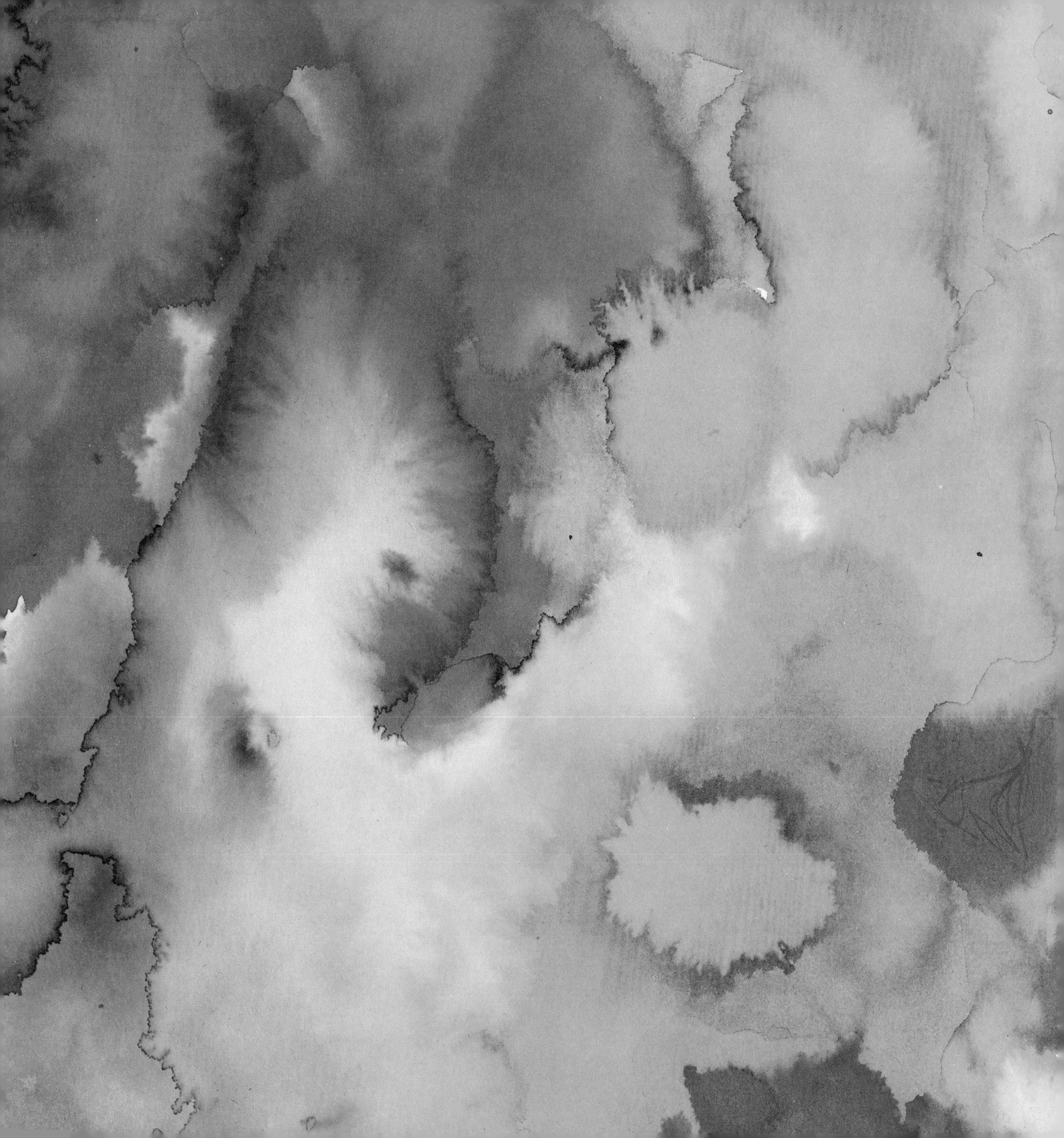

Little Funnies
Joke Time
What do you give a sick bird?
Tweetment!